Talia and the Tiny T Cells

by Jacqueline Palmer
and Matthew Taylor

Talia and the Tiny T Cells
Written by Jacqueline Palmer, Illustrated by Matthew Taylor
Copyright © 2020 Jacqueline Palmer, Matthew Taylor
South Bend, IN USA

Published by Ember Publishing House
ISBN: 978-1-952937-06-4
Library of Congress Control Number: 2020946130

In a time of uncertainty,

this book empowers young children with the scientific truth that their bodies are strong and capable of keeping them safe.

Talia was an active girl who liked to run and jump and play with her friends. She was happy and healthy.

Families of tiny T cells lived inside Talia's body. It was their job to protect Talia and keep her body safe.

One day, a small, sneaky virus crept inside, and the T cells did not notice.

When Talia woke up that day, she felt sick.

Her muscles were sore.
Her stomach was achy,
and she had a cough.

The virus had multiplied and now
there was a group of sneaky virus cells
hiding inside Talia's body. The virus
cells were so small that they could only
been seen with special magnifying
lenses

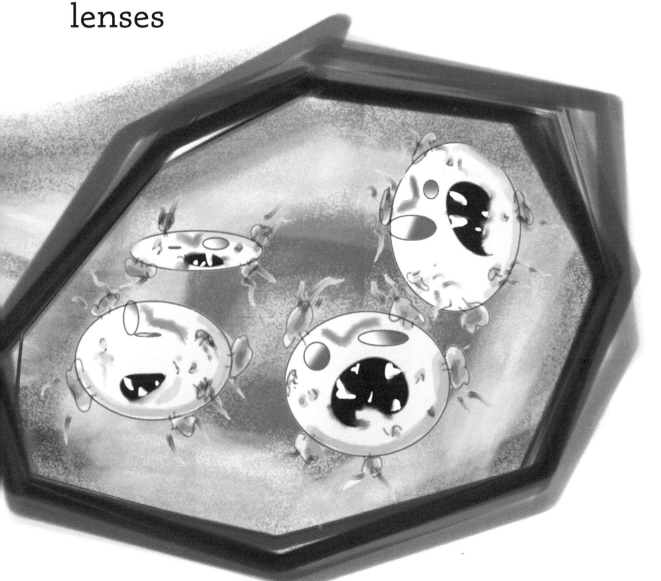

Talia decided to stay home and rest. She did not want to spread the virus to her friends. Her body also needed the extra energy to help her get better.

Meanwhile, deep inside Talia's body, the families of tiny T cells sprung into action.

The tiny T cells set off on their mission to find the small virus cells in Talia's body.

The first stop for the tiny T cells was inside Talia's arm.

They found nerve cells with long legs and muscle cells that lined up in stacks and rows. When Talia moved her arm, the long-legged nerve cells sent electrical signals to the muscle cells. The muscle cells gripped and pulled each other with their strong tiny arms.

The tiny T cells did not find the virus inside Talia's arm. "Everything looks healthy here!"

The tiny T cells hopped into a blood vessel to catch a ride to the next stop of their journey.

The tiny T cells quickly WOOSHED off on their way

"WHOA!"

In the vessel, small red blood cells surrounded the T cells. They noticed the red blood cells carrying loads of oxygen to the muscles and other parts of Talia's body.

The tiny T cells searched all around but did not find any virus cells.

"Everything looks healthy here!"

They zipped off to their next stop.

Next, the tiny T cells traveled deep inside Talia'
belly. They hopped off inside the intestines,
where food travels from the stomach.

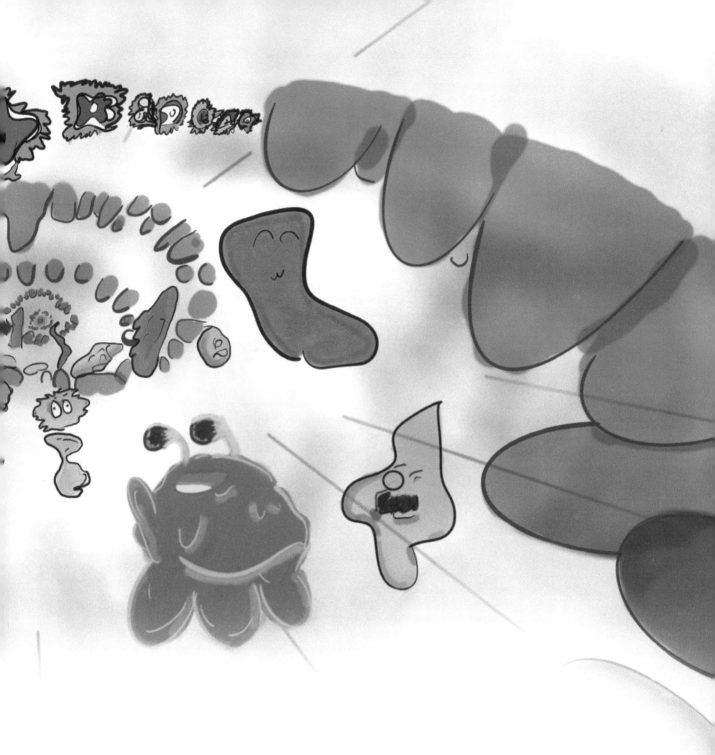

t was lively and bustling with activity. The walls were
packed with diverse cells of all shapes and sizes. These
cells were busy gathering up food particles and packaging
t up. The food would be used as building blocks for other
cells and energy in Talia's body so that she could run and
play.

Again, the T cells searched for the virus.

Suddenly, two young T cells jumped with surprise and called to the others, "We found the virus!"

Their mother came over to take a look. "No, this is not a virus cell.

This is a good bacteria cell that is helping our body break down food," she reassured them.

The tiny T cells hopped back inside the blood vessel and continued on their journey.

They searched each red blood cell for any sneaky cargo but did not find any virus cells.

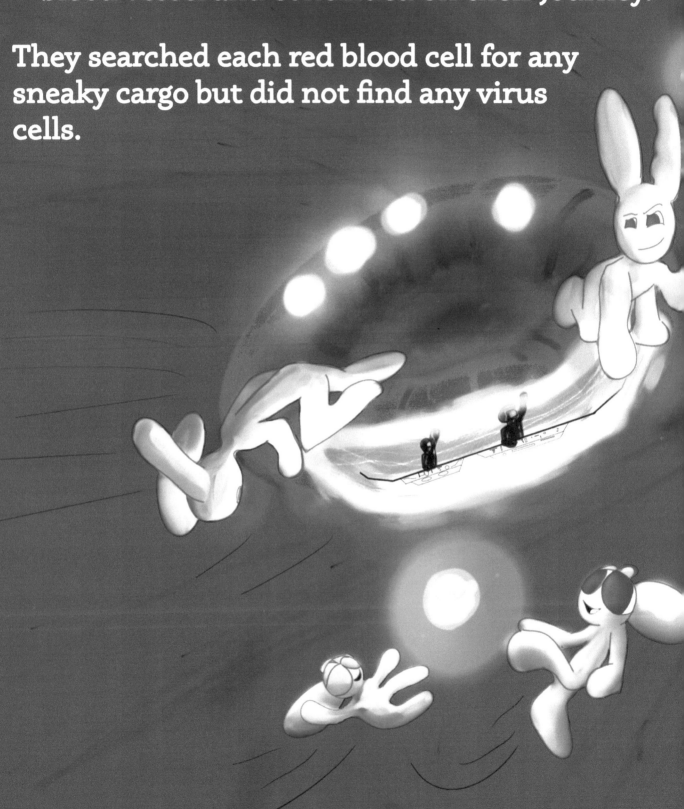

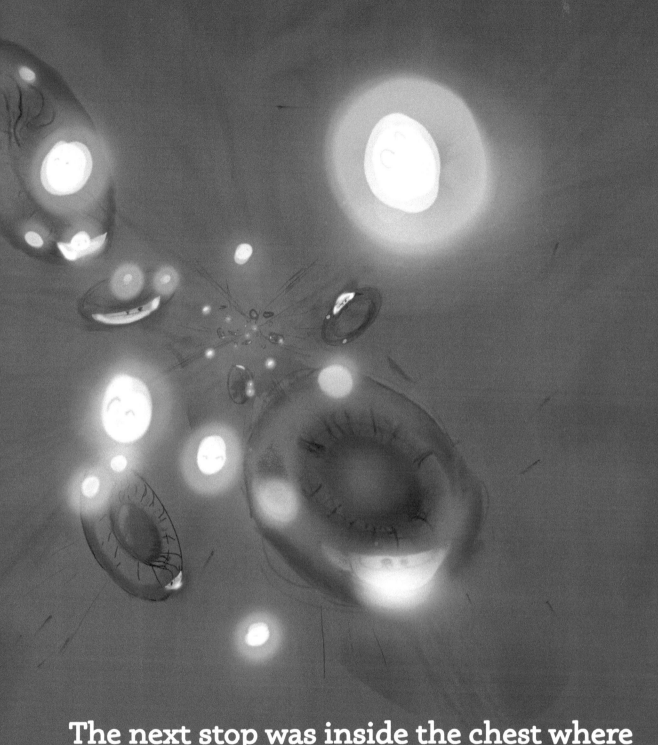

The next stop was inside the chest where
they would search the lungs.

Finally, the tiny T cells arrived inside her chest. They were alarmed to find the virus cells crowded together here and invading the lung cells.

The lung cells could not breathe! When they saw the T cells they cried out for help.

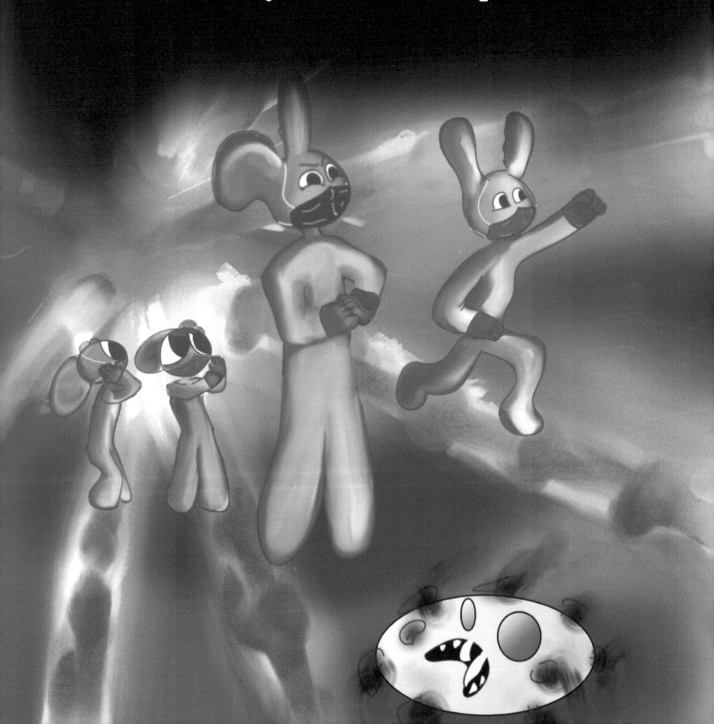

The tiny T cells leapt into battle mode!

They blasted the virus cells with special enzymes to deactivate it so that it could not move. They chiseled and picked the virus off the lung cells. Now the virus couldn't hurt any more cells in Talia's body.

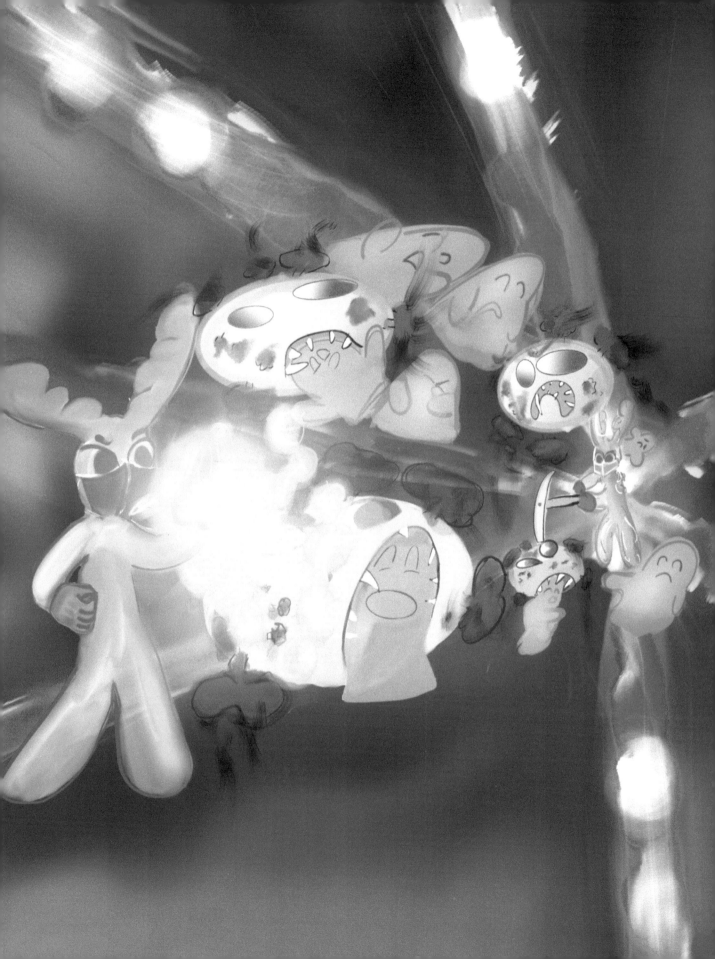

The lung cells could finally breathe again!

The tiny T cells felt proud of their hard work. They would always be there to defend Talia and her body.

The next morning, Talia woke up and felt much better.

She knew that her body was strong and that it would always work to protect her.

CPSIA information can be obtained
at www.ICGtesting.com
Printed in the USA
BVHW020536090421
604474BV00016B/208